Little

and the
fishermen

illustrated by Gordon Stowell

Jesus often walked by the lakeside, watching the birds and listening to the waves lapping on the beach. He liked to feel the wind on His face and the soft sand under His feet. He loved the beautiful world around Him.

He met some fishermen one day.
One of them was called Simon Peter.
They were cleaning up their nets
after a busy time fishing all through
the night.

Jesus spoke to them and they enjoyed
hearing what He said about God.

Soon a crowd gathered around and they asked Him to teach them as well.

"They will not all be able to hear," said Jesus. "I must get further away from them. Peter, push your boat out into the lake a little. I will sit in the boat and speak from there."

Peter pushed out the boat. Jesus settled down in it and began to speak to the people on the beach.

He spoke of many things. He told them how God loves them.

He taught them that God never leaves them and how they need never be frightened or worried.

The crowd listened and loved everything that Jesus told them.

After a while Jesus turned to Peter. "Take your boat further out into the deeper water. Let us catch some fish."

"Not much use in doing that," said
Peter. "We've been fishing all night
and caught nothing, but I will do as
you say."

They took the boat out into deeper
water. They put the nets over the
side and waited . . .

When they pulled up the nets there were so many fish that the nets broke!

Fish spilled all over the place. The birds screamed overhead and the fishermen cheered.

They had to get another boat to come and help, and there were so many fish the boats began to sink. Peter was scared and he knelt before Jesus. "Do not be afraid," said Jesus.

"Come and follow me." When they got back to the beach the fishermen left everything and followed Jesus.

You can find this story in Luke chapter 5, verses 1–11.

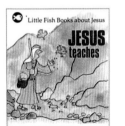

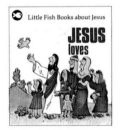

 Little Fish Books